FORWARD

This book was discovered in the library of Edith Kinney Gaylord after her death in January 2001 by Louise G. and Clayton I. Bennett. The book was given to Aubrey K. McClendon, Chairman and Chief Executive Officer of Chesapeake Energy Corporation and personal friend of the Bennetts. Mr. McClendon contacted Bob Blackburn, Executive Director of the Oklahoma Historical Society for assistance in having the book reprinted. Mr. Blackburn engaged Julie Washam of Chesapeake Energy Corporation and Jeff Behymer of Park Hill Publishing to assist with the reprinting of the book.

The book was reprinted in a limited edition of 5,000 copies in July 2005 with Chesapeake Energy Corporation underwriting the cost of the reprint.

Please read and enjoy the fascinating history of the Oklahoma City Oil field, a true giant in the history of the oil business and a great source of wealth creation in Oklahoma City.

—Aubrey K. McClendon

June 2005

The OKLAHOMA CITY OIL FIELD
in pictures

Compiled by

JACK LANCE, Inc.

January 1931

Published by

JACK LANCE, INC.
ADVERTISING
OKLAHOMA CITY

Printed by

TRAVE-TAYLOR CO.

OKLAHOMA CITY

The Discovery Well

ITIO's Oklahoma City #1
December 4, 1928; 5,500 bbls/day

Compliments
of
Wirt Franklin
Petroleum
Corporation
♦ ♦
Ardmore and
Oklahoma
City

RELATION of the story of the Oklahoma City Oil Field, essentially must be aligned closely with scientific development. It is a narrative of the victory of science and practical geology over the forces of Nature in a new and gigantic operation that has become an epic in the history of oil development. Although the discovery and rapid development of the Oklahoma City Field is a story rich in human interest, the effort of the publishers has been to weld fact and feature, word and picture, into a truthful and, withal, an interesting narrative of modern oil exploration.

—*The Publishers*
January 1931

"THAR SHE BLOWS!''

The triumphant bellow of the grizzled New Bedford whaler roars across the angry waves while his mates scurry to prepare harpoons and tack sails for pursuit of the oily prize.

"Thar she blows!"

The roar of frenzied drillers as preliminary underground rumblings herald approach of a gushing flood the while they scurry in preparation to trap the golden flow.

The exultant cry is age old to the men who seek in far places or delve in great depths for oil. The scene is older. But, whether it be to seamed New Bedford whaler or seasoned southwestern driller, the thrill it presages is ever new.
And, like the monster whale, once the world's sole source of oil, the gigantic petroleum gusher today announces itself with spouting plume.

"Thar she blows!"

So came the Oklahoma City Oil Field into being at three o'clock on the afternoon of December 4, 1928.

Workers scampering in all directions, reporters, newspaper photographers, lease scouts. Pandemonium.

At first a stream of water rises high above the crown block, subsides a moment, then climbs even higher, changing slowly to a darker color and finally becomes a steady geyser of golden brown liquid.

Cameras click. Newswriters race madly to a rural telephone. The news is relayed to editorial rooms of the nation's newspapers. Twenty-seven years of effort have been rewarded. Oklahoma City has its first real oil! From the bottom of a hole extending nearly 7,000 feet into the earth a golden fountain aggregating 5,000 barrels daily is bursting.

It is a far cry from that day in 1859 when Edwin L. Drake drilled in the first producing oil well in the United States, situated at Titusville, Pennsylvania. Down the horizon of Time, the Monarch, OIL, has moved, gradually, steadily, keeping pace with the demand of an evergrowing nation, a demand that became worldwide with an ever enlarging need of oil for fuel, for lubrication, for a thousand and one other uses that have developed as supply increased.

Today, oil is being produced in nineteen of the forty-eight states in the nation. Of the nineteen, three loom largest in the history of petroleum production— Oklahoma, Texas and California.

First oil in Oklahoma was found in 1902 near Bartlesville, the home office of the Indian Territory Illuminating Oil Company which brought in the dis-

covery well in the Oklahoma City field. Slowly but steadily, after that beginning, the depths of areas throughout the state have been plumbed. Many thousands of dollars went into the ground never to be recovered. But, many times, also, perseverance and faith of prospectors were rewarded. Glen Pool, Cushing, Healdton, Bristow, Burbank, Tonkawa, Garber, Cromwell, Seminole—all names to conjure with in the history of oil.

County after county developed production, but in the county where stood the state's capitol, the search continued to produce only a string of abandoned "dusters." Enthusiasm waxed with the spudding of each new test and became disappointment with each abandoned hole.

But the search, first begun in 1903, continued, notwithstanding a statement issued by a government geologist that while he believed there was oil near Oklahoma City, it lay too deep ever to be developed commercially.

Many cities had been "made" by the discovery of oil in sections adjacent to them. Tulsa, magic capital of the oil world, had grown from a mere Indian trading post to a magnificent city.

Oklahoma City's citizenship said: "We have here a marvelous city, the center of a rich agricultural section. A large jobbing center with many factories; the most complete terminal and transportation facilities in Oklahoma. In our diversification of industry, we lack only oil to complete the picture."

Faced with difficulties and obstacles which seemed at times insurmountable, defying the opinion of an acknowledged geological leader of his day, combatting a skepticism which at times made the extensive financial backing necessary for the admittedly deeper drilling, difficult to obtain, hardy petroleum pioneers pursued their quest.

For years their dream did not materialize. Thousands of dollars were spent. Disappointment followed disappointment. Still the search went on.

Then, at last, fate broke with a vengeance in Oklahoma City's favor. After approximately twenty-five dry holes

Close inspection of the top picture will reveal the checkerboarded location of wells like the shocks in a corn field. In the foreground is the "slush pit" from which the rotary mud is pumped by the "mud hogs." In the center is a view provided by Noble and Olsen, drilling contractors, showing their new type Emsco draw works. Below is one of the most striking pictures of a scene at dawn ever obtained in the field. Steam from exhausts, as far as eye can reach, indicates the industry of thousands of men throughout the night. The monster derrick in the foreground is designed by the O'Brien Construction Company.

had been drilled—an average of almost one a year for the twenty-seven years devoted to the exploration, there opened at the very doors of the city a pool that has proved the marvel of the oil world of today.

On November 1, 1930, the I. T. I. O. discovery well had shown the way to 613 producing wells with an estimated potential flow of close to 2,800,000 barrels of oil daily, with approximately 145 additional wells in process of drilling.

Buried treasure totalling more than forty million dollars, which had lain hidden for years in the door yard of Oklahoma City had been wrested from its long hiding place and carried into the marts of the world, recapitulation of September 1, 1930, revealed. On that date, a total of 31,-691,097 barrels of high gravity crude had passed through the separators and into pipelines which convey it to national and international markets.

At an average price of $1.35 a barrel this represented wealth totalling $42,782,980.95. And, this took place in the face of the most drastic proration schedule the oil world has ever experienced, a schedule which necessitated reduction of production to as low as five percent of the potential open flow of the field.

It might be well to delve for a moment into the field's potentialities. This term, "potential production" is one oil men are chary of using, because it may be so easily misunderstood. By way of explanation, it may be said that when a well is first brought in, it is allowed to flow for a certain number of hours, perhaps ten, maybe a full twenty-four. Its flow is gauged during that time. Assuming that the gauge shows a flow of 1,000 barrels an hour for a twenty-four hour period, the well is rated at a potential flow of 24,000 barrels a day.

However, many things may occur to disturb the original normal flow of this well, should it again be allowed to produce to capacity. Offset wells, drilled on nearby leases may diminish its flow. Wells have been known to come in as large producers only to dwindle to nothing when reopened after being shut down for a long period.

Mastodon of all drilling bits, shown above, is properly termed a rock bit and sometimes does well to drill a foot an hour. Second view is an emergency casinghead packing box designed by Hinderliter Tool Company to prevent leakage of gas and oil and reduce pressure and attendant danger. The bailer brings up all sorts of rock particles from the hole as does the circulating mud. The machine in the center, designed by Brauer Machine Works, separates foreign matter in the slush pit. Below is an upright view of the rock bit shown above.

However, upon the above basis, the potential flow of the city field on November 1, 1930, was 2,800,000 barrels a day as estimated by competent oil statisticians. At a price of $1.35 a barrel, this would amount to $5,780,000 in a single day, $173,400,000 in a single month or $2,080,800,-000 in a year. These figures describe more accurately than any group of lurid adjectives the true magnitude of this field.

Oklahoma is a state of pioneers. Mr. E. W. Marland's generous gift to the citizens of this state and to the nation at large of the magnificent statue of the Pioneer Woman was symbolic of the pioneer spirit that has prevailed in Oklahoma ever since its opening to settlement. The great oil pools that have been developed within the state's borders all came as a reward of pioneering.

Reverting to the history of petroleum pioneering in Oklahoma County which is recorded as having first begun in 1903 as nearly as history can agree, the writings of Dr. Charles N. Gould, director of the Oklahoma Geological Survey, as contained in Bulletin No. 40-SS, published in May, 1930, are interesting. In this, Dr. Gould says: "It very often happens that differences of opinion arise regarding the discovery of the structure of an oil field. The Oklahoma City field is no exception. I have been at some pains to endeavor to sift out the claims of the structure at Oklahoma City. The statements herewith represent my best judgment in the matter."

Speaking then of the earliest well drilled in Oklahoma County, Dr. Gould says:

"The first well drilled in Oklahoma County to reach a depth of over 500 feet, was located one-fourth mile south of Spencer. The company which financed the well was organized by E. J. Streeter, a hardware merchant in Oklahoma City, who was the moving factor of the organization. L. C. Hivick was the contractor. The well was drilled in 1903 and reached a reported depth of 2,002 feet. "From time to time, other wells were drilled in Oklahoma and adjoining counties. Six wells drilled in Oklahoma County are reported in earlier Geological Survey reports.

L. E. Trout, above, first mapped a structure of the Oklahoma City field back in 1917. He had sufficient faith in his findings to form a company and drill a well, known as the Firestone, in the south end of the present field. The well went only to 4,000 feet and was a "dry hole," but huge deep gushers have been brought in nearby since discovery of the field. Trout now is chief geologist for C. C. Julian Oil & Royalty Company. W. W. Claussen, chief geologist in this district for I. T. I. O. is shown next with John Derden, I. T. I. O. geologist, another early student of this area, below.

All were located without geological advice and for the most part were drilled by promoters and financed by local capital."

Mr. Hivick, today, is drilling in Sunset Park addition, two miles west of proven territory in the Oklahoma City pool. He is authority for the statement that while the Spencer test was under way, a test was started at the edge of Arcadia, on the strength of a pocket of gas encountered in drilling a water well. He adds that the first Arcadia test was followed by two others, the three tests being in Section 28, Township 14, Range 1 West.

According to the best information available, thoughts of oil production in Oklahoma County encountered a lapse after these few early tests until October 31, 1913, when the Merchants Oil and Gas Company of Oklahoma City began drilling a test in Section 5, Township 11 North, Range 2 West, and on June 25, 1914, abandoned the hole at 3,001 feet, with no worthwhile showing having been encountered. This dry hole was drilled about three miles north and a half-mile east of the I. T. I. O. gusher completed December 4, 1928, the discovery well of the Oklahoma City field.

In 1915 a test was drilled to 2,100 feet on the Oliver Black farm, in the southwest quarter of Section 34, Township 14, Range 1 East, about a mile and one-half south of Luther.

Next the Mutual Oil and Gas Company was formed for the purpose of drilling a test well near Oklahoma City, the location selected being in Section 7, Township 12 North, Range 2 West. This well was drilled to 2,925 feet. Gas was struck at 2,900 feet, but of insufficient flow to justify much deeper drilling. G. A. Nichols, prominent realtor of Oklahoma City, was one of the chief backers of this test, which was completed in 1916.

In 1917 a well was spudded in on the Charles Aspland farm in Section 25, Township 13 North, Range 4 West, about three miles west of Britton. No other drilling was done on this test.

Dr. G. E. Anderson, teacher of geology in the University of Oklahoma and member of the geological department of the Indian Territory Illuminating Oil Company, worked out an early structure of the Oklahoma City field. Below him is shown John E. Van Dall, chief geologist for Sinclair Oil and Refining Company, who worked the structure north of the City on which a small producer was drilled several years ago. E. A. Paschal, chief geologist for Coline Oil Company, shown below, was active in some of the earlier geological findings in the field.

Beginning in 1919 the scene of activity in the quest for oil in Oklahoma County switched to the State Center, three miles east of Jones. Drilling was in progress for about two or three years in this area, but with no definite results.

In 1921, the Idaho Drilling Company drilled to a depth of about 1,600 feet in Section 17-14N-3W, about three miles west and two miles north of Edmond. Again, no results. In the same year the Dixie Oil Company and the Big Three Oil Company drilled to about the same depth in Section 31-12N-2W, east of Oklahoma City, but to no avail.

Then, in 1924, W. R. Ramsey, head of the Ramsey Petroleum Corporation, one of the largest and most successful operators in Oklahoma and Texas, completed a dry hole at 3,990 feet in Section 8-12N-1W, about three miles west of Spencer. This was the most costly test drilled in Oklahoma County up to that time.

During the same year the Firestone Oil Company completed another dry hole at about 4,000 feet in Section 36-11N-3W, about two miles south of the discovery gusher of the present day field.

In 1925 the Maxine Petroleum Company started a well in Section 9-14N-1W, two miles north of Arcadia. After drilling and shutting down over a period of about eighteen months, this well was taken over by the HomaOkla Oil Company of Oklahoma City, which drilled to a depth of 4,500 feet when it encountered water.

Two miles west and three miles south of Choctaw, due south of what is now Nicoma Park, W. R. Ramsey tried in 1927, drilling in Section 9-11N-1W, to a depth of 4,512 feet, but again to no avail. It was in this same year that Wirt Franklin and Joe I. Cromwell shut down at 4,534 feet in Section 21-14N-3W, two miles west and a mile north of Edmond.

Inasmuch as the above locations and efforts at finding oil in Oklahoma County lead up to the actual achievement, it

Another gusher—one of the 400. The background is a view of good cotton and corn ground, but the wind is waving a bigger stalk than ever has grown before. Some wells have two separators, some three, and big ones necessitate four. They separate the gas from the oil as it comes from the well. A rare scene is that next from the last. In the background is the Mary Sudik running wild and the pool in the foreground is oil collected in the eleven days this monster sprayed the countryside. Hastily erected tanks are shown below yet, withal, presenting an impression of finished installation made possible by the ingenuity of manufacturers.

is well to turn back to the history of those who shared in the actual finding, those pioneers of the oil industry, the geologists. Quoting again from Dr. Charles N. Gould of the Oklahoma Geological Survey, in his Bulletin No. 40-SS, we find that he says:

"The two geologists who first observed a favorable oil structure near Oklahoma City were probably George D. Morgan and Jerry B. Newby. The exact dates when these first observations were made seem to have been lost. Morgan says, 'In either 1917 or 1919, and I cannot remember which year, I worked out the structure at Oklahoma City.' Everett Carpenter, to whom Morgan referred me, says, 'I am of the opinion it was about 1917.' Newby, who also worked out the structure, says, 'My work north and northeast of Oklahoma City was done in the early part of 1919.' "L. E. Trout, in the fall of 1919, made a reconnoissance of the area and later in 1920 or early in 1921 mapped an area in southern Oklahoma and northern Cleveland Counties in what is now the southern part of the Oklahoma City field. This seems to have been the first structure map prepared on the region. With Trout were associated S. H. Woods, Claude Dalley, and his brother, L. R. Trout. In 1925, a well located by Trout in Section 35-11N-2W, near the Cleveland County line, was drilled to a depth of 4,480 feet. Several minor shows of oil were reported.

"In 1925 John R. Bunn worked out a surface high north of the State Capitol and a deep test (7,180 feet) drilled by Cromwell-Franklin, Thompson No. 1, found water in the Wilcox. This well had several minor shows in shallower horizons. An earlier well drilled not far away is the discovery well of Oklahoma County.

"E. A. Paschal in 1926, while employed by the Coline Company, traced the Hennessey-Garber contact and recognized the presence of a fold south of Oklahoma City. Upon the recommendation of C. T. Moore, then chief geologist of the company, three leases were purchased in the area, all of which are now producing.

"So the presence of a structure lying north, northeast, and southeast of Oklahoma City has been a matter of general

The driller's best friend and his most feared foe is one and the same—water. He wants plenty on top of the ground and none at all at the bottom of the hole. Water for drilling, boilers and mud is provided in the latest improved equipment—turn a crank and there it is. Next is shown one of the newer installations in the field. The white color on these separators is not paint, it is frost. Gas pressure operates here on the same principle as your kitchen refrigerator. The usual conception of a pipe line is a line of pipe. But pipe lines carrying gas and oil from this field are almost as complicated as a watch as evidenced by the variety of gadgets in the lower picture.

geologic knowledge for several years, and a number of geologists not mentioned herewith have at various times noted the structure . . .''

As has been said introductory to Dr. Gould's report, there are some who played a part in geological work in Oklahoma County who are not given full and sufficient credit in that report. For example, Dr. Gould says, ''In 1925 John R. Bunn worked out a surface high north of the state capital.'' John Van Dall, now with the Sinclair Oil and Gas Company, worked with Bunn in this effort, according to most geologists in the Oklahoma City territory. Through their joint efforts Joe I. Cromwell was interested to the extent of blocking a tract of 5,000 acres in that vicinity.

But considerably prior to that, back in 1917, most geologists agree, L. E. Trout, following the Garber trend, had believed there was oil in Oklahoma County. He predicated this belief upon his geological findings southeast of Oklahoma City. He mapped a structure at what is now the south end of the field.

While engaged in field work in preparation for a bulletin on the geology of Cleveland and McClain counties, Dr. G. E. Anderson was able to trace in the field the stratigraphic horizon now known as the Hennessey-Garber Contact through these counties. Later, while in charge of field work for the Indian Territory Illuminating Oil Company in Western Oklahoma, he traced this contact from the town of Garber, south through Logan and Oklahoma Counties. This work revealed an offset in the contact just south of Oklahoma City, the north end being some seven or eight miles west of the contact as traced north from Cleveland County.

This condition had two possible interpretations: that the north end was a ledge of sandstone projecting southerly in the Hennessey shale or that there was a southerly projecting structural nose which caused the offset.

That the first of these possibilities was not true, he proved by carefully tracing the sandstone through Oklahoma City

Some of the largest gushers in the field have been brought in from the sand formations outlying the Arbuckle limestone in which the discovery well was found. This structure underlies the North Canadian river. Above is a flood scene with two locations accessible only by boat, built on improvised foundations. Center picture shows how 20,000 barrels of oil a day will act up under 150,000,000 cubic feet of gas pressure. Starting an oil well is like building a skyscraper. First a basement or "cellar" must be dug. The "clam shell" in the lower scene, mounted on a truck, demonstrates another innovation in speed.

north into the true Garber sand. The Garber trend was then traced through Oklahoma City by means of excavations for buildings as the piers in the Petroleum Building and excavations for the Bell Telephone Company building both rest on the Garber. A few actual outcrops of the Garber also were found in the city, one of the most prominent being on the north side of the railroad yards and just west of the Walnut street viaduct.

By tracing east from Capitol Hill on G Avenue, the large rock outcrops in Trosper Park were interpreted as Garber sandstone, for by continuing east the Hennessey shale made a large embayment extending north to near the town of Spencer. Trosper Park was interpreted as the top of this structure. So, finally, was the large southerly projecting nose in the Garber sandstone proved.

To the geologist, this was a very large structure approximately 400 feet higher than the normal westerly dip and in an area extending from north of the Capitol to the south side of Section 25-11 North-3 West. Recommendation by Dr. Anderson was that acreage be leased covering an area two miles west and four miles north from the southeast corner of Section 25-11 North-3 West.

The importance of his interpretation was quickly recognized by the Indian Territory Illuminating Oil Company and leasing began immediately. After some 6,000 acres had been leased, detailing work was started and this work confirmed in all particulars Dr. Anderson's earlier reconnaissance. Following this work, location for the discovery well was made in the south east of Section 24-11 North 3 West.

Had it not been for this very large structural feature, some eight miles long, over two miles wide and 400 feet high. it is very doubtful if drilling would have been carried to such a great depth as the general consensus of geologic opinion was that the Wilcox sand in this area—the objective of all deep drilling in Western Oklahoma—would be entirely too deep to be reached by the drill.

However, such opinion did not take into account that struc-

The layman may think it peculiar that a hole be drilled and then cemented shut again. However, it is necessary in deep wells. The casing is anchored for strength at the base of the completed well. Above is shown the plug which is lowered to the bottom of the casing through which cement is forced by special pressure machinery. This view is by courtesy of the Halliburton Oil Well Cementing Company, specializing in this work all over the world. Over the hill and far away go pipe lines from the field. Here is a gang on the "firing line," traveling welder and everything except the "canal wrench" outfit. Below is a close-up of an unruly gusher in the process of being tamed.

WIRT FRANKLIN

Wirt Franklin, president of Wirt Franklin Petroleum Corporation and vice-president and general manager of Cromwell-Franklin Oil Company, is nationally known as president of the Independent Petroleum Association in which capacity he won recognition before Congress in his masterly presentation of facts on conservation and the necessity for tariff on crude oil. Mr. Franklin was associated with Joe Cromwell in the drilling of the first deep test north of the State Capitol leading up to the discovery of the Oklahoma City field. He is a producer, refiner and marketer of petroleum products and as such, recognized as one of the leading exponents of true conservation of petroleum in the United States.

The extensive operations of the Wirt Franklin petroleum Corporation are mainly in charge of these men: Top, left: Frank Head, vice president in charge of the land department; right, top: Chester Franklin, vice president and manager of refinery sales. Center row, Frank M. Porter, vice president and production manager; Glenn Grimes, chief geologist and E. J. McKee, petroleum engineer. Bottom, left: A. M. Edmiston, director and refinery superintendent; bottom, right: Edward Galt, secretary and assistant treasurer.

tures usually become higher with depth and the Oklahoma City structure was no exception for drilling data now shows the structure to be at least 1,800 feet high on the Arbuckle lime.

This was the beginning of what has since proved to be one of the world's greatest oil pools.

C. L. Wagner, J. H. Derden, geologist, C. W. Roop, I. T. I. O. land man, and R. J. Riggs, chief geologist for I. T. I. O. all cooperated in this work.

Perhaps it would be wise to interpolate here that the advance of the oil industry accounts in a large measure for the actual discovery of the Oklahoma City field. Garber had been found. The trend indicated a direction toward Oklahoma City, through Marshall and Crescent in Logan County. Handicapped to a great extent by the fact that drilling tools in the earlier history of Oklahoma County did not permit of really deep tests, as deep, in fact, as the pool of oil and gas has been found to rest in Oklahoma County, there was small probability that the earlier efforts could be successful. In fact, it was practically impossible. But the advance of the oil industry has produced more efficient drilling tools, capable of boring to a much greater depth and this has accompanied the efforts of this county with final achievement. Add to this that the oil industry, like other businesses, must expand logically and gradually, which it did as indications looked toward Oklahoma County, and therein you have the real secret of ultimate success in development of the Oklahoma City field.

With the No. 1 Edwards test, north of the State Capitol, actually completed for a flow of approximately fifty barrels of oil a day, late in 1926, interest in the attempt to find oil in actually paying quantities increased to fever heat in Oklahoma County.

The Cromwell-Franklin Oil Company came into being when Joe I. Cromwell, after many efforts to interest other big companies in the Oklahoma City field had failed, turned to Wirt Franklin of Ardmore, head of the Wirt Franklin

Joe I. Cromwell, president of Cromwell-Franklin Oil Company, above, together with Wirt Franklin, president of Wirt Franklin Petroleum Corporation and Mr. Cromwell's business associate, uncovered the first actual oil production found in Oklahoma County with the drilling in of the No. 1 Edwards test for a flow of fifty barrels daily, late in 1926. Mr. Cromwell, several years earlier, opened the Cromwell oil pool near Wewoka.

R. R. Owens, second picture, is gas engineer for Wirt Franklin Petroleum Corporation and Cromwell-Franklin Oil Company.

Below is Harry Franklin, vice-president and general manager of Capitol Drilling Company.

Petroleum Corporation. Mr. Franklin became interested and the joint company was formed.

Today the Cromwell-Franklin Oil Company and the Wirt Franklin Petroleum Corporation operate approximately 50 wells in the pool. One of these producing wells, the Lowry No. 2, had produced more than 1,000,000 barrels of oil on November 1, 1930.

Wirt Franklin Petroleum Corporation has under lease in the Oklahoma City field more than 400 acres, 98 per cent of which is proven territory. In addition, the company has under lease more than 40,000 acres on trends of geology in various parts of the state and has more than 200 producing wells in southern Oklahoma.

Mr. Franklin is president of the Wirt Franklin Petroleum Corporation, which is capitalized for $10,000,000, with headquarters at Ardmore. He is vice-president and general manager of the Cromwell-Franklin Oil Company with headquarters in the Franklin building, Oklahoma City, a seven story structure in the heart of the business district owned by Wirt Franklin; in addition, the Southern Drilling Company is a firm whose stock is owned entirely by the Wirt Franklin Petroleum Corporation. Also, Mr. Franklin is president of the Independent Petroleum Association; president of the Oklahoma City pro-ration Committee, and a director in the American Petroleum Institute. Other officials and department heads of the company include: Frank M. Porter, vice-president and production manager; Frank M. Head, vice-president, assistant secretary and manager of the Land Department of the Wirt Franklin Petroleum Corporation; Edward Galt, secretary and assistant treasurer; Chester A. Franklin, vice-president and manager of wholesale sales; A. M. Edmiston, director and refinery superintendent; R. R. Owens, gas engineer, superintendent of drilling for the Southern Drilling Company; Eddie Cope, production superintendent for the Oklahoma City district; Harry Franklin, vice-president and general manager of the Capitol Drilling Company, another subsidiary of the Wirt Franklin organization; and Joe I. Cromwell, president of the Cromwell-Franklin Oil Company.

Wirt Franklin Petroleum Corporation combines all phases of the oil industry—producing, refining and marketing. At the top is a view of this company's gasoline plant on the famous Lowery lease in the Oklahoma City field. Next below is the crew of the Lowery No. 2, a well that has produced more than a million barrels of oil. Third is a picture of one of the many Palacine gasoline stations which dot the state. Next is shown one of the company's tank cars used to transport its products. Last view is a battery of Clark Compressors in the Lowery plant.

The Wirt Franklin Petroleum Corporation owns and operates a 4,000 barrel capacity refinery located on a 200 acre tract at Ardmore. It operates more than 200 retail service stations in many sections of the state.

To the Indian Territory Illuminating Oil Company of Bartlesville, Oklahoma, must go the credit for actual discovery of the Oklahoma City field. While the first oil found in Oklahoma County was that in Cromwell-Franklin's No. 1 Edwards north of the state capitol, the discovery well of the main field was I. T. I. O's. Oklahoma City No. 1, which came in December 4, 1928, for approximately 5,500 barrels a day.

Since that time, I. T. I. O. has drilled and is drilling many wells. Statistics as of November 1, 1930, showed this firm to have 245 producing oil wells in the Oklahoma City field, 13 producers being worked over, 15 gas wells and 29 drilling operations. These are wells of which I. T. I. O. is sole owner.

In addition, this company, with Cromwell-Franklin, owns a joint interest in a number of other producers and drilling wells.

Charles E. Carter, formerly district land man for the I. T. I. O. in the Oklahoma City district, recalls an occasion in 1919 when he was driving through a part of what is now the world's greatest oil field. His family were with him. One of the girls observed two huge outcroppings of red sandstone on either side of the road. She exclaimed, "Oh, see the Golden Gates!"

"Golden Gates" they have proved to be to thousands of oil men and residents of Oklahoma County.

Eight years later this same outcrop of rocks attracted the attention of a geological party of the I. T. I. O. and under the direction of R. J. Riggs and Dr. G. E. Anderson, a preliminary geological study was made of the entire territory surrounding them. As a result of their surveys, instructions were issued to secure the leases on a block of approximately 10,000 acres covering all of the structure which indicated prospects were good for finding oil at a reasonable depth.

The proximity of the source of crude oil and the finished product is graphically shown in the first picture above, a scene at a Wirt Franklin gasoline plant. The tower at the left is for cooling water in the manufacture of gasoline. One of the thousand-gallon tank trucks used for the transportation of the finished products is shown in the second view. On the left in the third picture is Mark Feeney, field superintendent of Southern Drilling Company, subsidiary of Wirt Franklin Petroleum Corporation. His companion is Eddie Cope, production superintendent for the Wirt Franklin and the Cromwell-Franklin companies. Below, another close-up view of the mechanics of a modern gasoline plant.

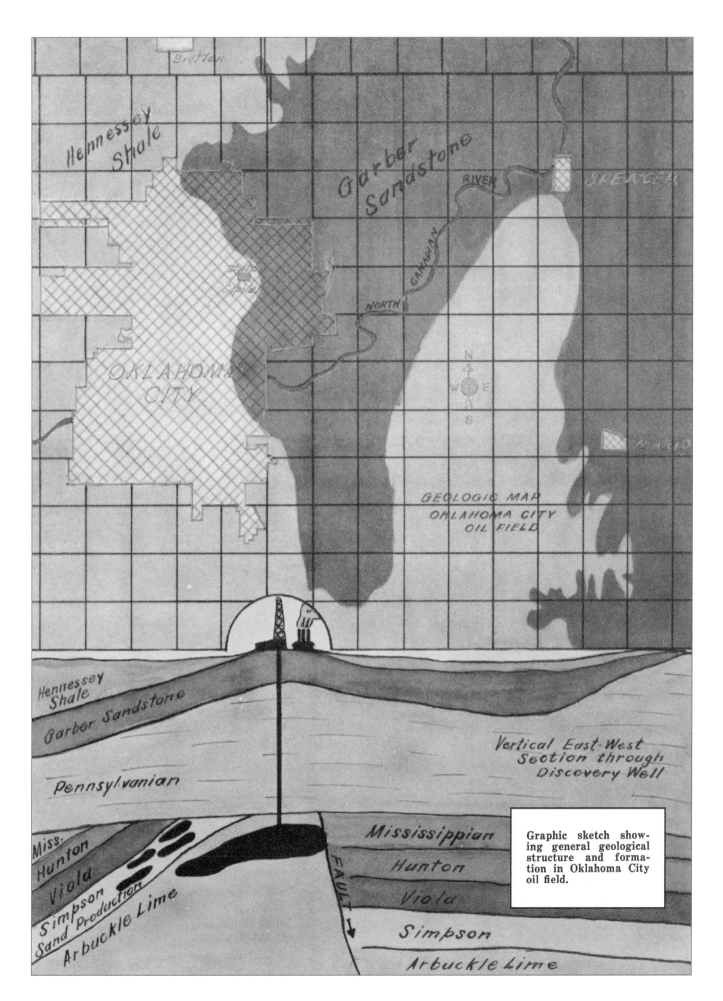

Graphic sketch showing general geological structure and formation in Oklahoma City oil field.

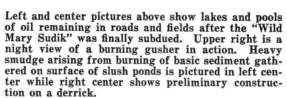

Left and center pictures above show lakes and pools of oil remaining in roads and fields after the "Wild Mary Sudik" was finally subdued. Upper right is a night view of a burning gusher in action. Heavy smudge arising from burning of basic sediment gathered on surface of slush ponds is pictured in left center while right center shows preliminary construction on a derrick.

Below are three graphic views of a burning gas well. Lower left shows close-up of the inferno created when a tink spark comes into contact with 150,000,000 cubic feet of gas. Note steam vapor which is being played on the flame and the sheet-iron "lean-to" where asbestos-clad firefighters receive temporary shelter from terrific heat of the blaze. A clear view of the giant torch is shown, center, and lower right shows crumpled derrick which melted like wax under first attack of the flaming gas.

The hardy crew in the above group worked eleven days and nights to control "Wild Mary Sudik," a modern "Shot heard round the World." Column after column of news reporting its defiance of man-made attempts to curb its pressure was carried on the front pages of the world's largest newspapers. In the center are Vincent and Mary Sudik, owners of the erstwhile farm land on which the well is lo-

cated. Below are grouped two shifts of drillers, the day and night "tours," who brought in this phenomenal gusher. In the center on the left, dressed in "store clothes" and with glasses, is W. P. "Pat" Sutton, superintendent of oil production for the Indian Territory Illuminating Oil Company, recognized as one of the most famous field bosses in the industry.

Later inquiry revealed that almost the entire structure was cut up into small acreage tracts and town lots. It took the greater part of a year and one-half for Mr. Carter and his associates to secure the leases, and to assemble the small tracts into consolidated units of forty acres or more suitable for modern economical drilling. Obtaining these leases was a peculiar task. Many of the land owners worked in the city. Obviously, the leasing could not be discussed with them during their work hours. This necessitated calls at their rural homes during the night-time. Imagine having to see several hundred persons out of normal work hours, leaving the state to see some, having to make repeat calls to see many. Long, hard, arduous toil—a chapter of the field that has been largely unsung. But it is what the I. T. I. O. had to do before it could even consider putting down the original well.

It was necessary to convince owners of the necessity of co-operation in signing leases in order to enable the company to undertake the tremendous expense attendant on a thorough deep test of the structure. However, a majority of landowners soon recognized the sincerity of the company and joined in active co-operation toward assembling of the acreage.

The first showing in the test well was encountered at 3,997 feet, on July 21, 1928, when a flow of gas estimated at 35,000,000 cubic feet a day attracted widespread interest. This interest increased rapidly as drilling progressed. Where gas is found it is usually a safe assumption that oil exists in the vicinity.

The discovery well had just penetrated a deep sand when, at 6,402 feet it blew in as Oklahoma City's first oil producer, flowing almost 6,000 barrels of oil in its first twenty-four hour test.

December 12, 1928, Empire Gas and Fuel Company completed a pipeline from the well to a railroad loading rack, five miles away, and the first oil was run from the new pool.

Above is a close-up of a rotary table. Tractors play an important part in development of the field. The caterpillar in the second picture is shown creeping through the mud as it slowly elevates the crown block pulley to its seat on top of the derrick. "Wild Mary" Sudik is properly chained in the next view. American Iron and Machine Works and Hughes Tool Company developed this special muzzle after the well had burst all ordinary shackles. Below, huge pipeline used to transport oil from the field is shown fording a river.

The tremendous quantities of gas encountered both in the upper sand and in the oil horizon emphasized the commercial importance of establishment of natural or "casinghead" gasoline reduction plants in the field for the purpose of condensing the rich gasoline vapor found in the gas into commercial gasoline and in March, 1928, I. T. I. O. began operation of the first plant of this nature. Establishment of other plants followed quickly.

This company recently completed and occupied a $100,000 office building situated in the shadow of the field. On August 1, 1930, the Indian Territory Illuminating Oil Company maintained a force of approximately 3,000 persons in the conduct of its various activities in the field.

H. V. Foster, president, and Burdette Blue, vice-president and general manager of the Indian Territory Illuminating Oil Company, maintain their offices at Bartlesville, the home office of the company.

Chief officials in the Oklahoma City district include: A. V. Hoenig, vice-president in charge of production; W. P. Sutton, superintendent of oil production, Oklahoma City district. John J. Lawry, district superintendent, North Oklahoma City district; Clyde O. DeVerse, district superintendent, South Oklahoma City district; C. M. Rader and S. M. Gilkey, assistants to Vice-President Hoenig; E. H. Carter, chief automotive mechanic; R. B. Wheeler, foreman, fuel and gas supply, Oklahoma City district; T. A. Stevens, superintendent of gas lift plant, gasoline plant and water department; Paul C. Wallack, construction engineer; C. E. Wright, chief petroleum engineer; J. Gus Patton, chief civil engineer; J. P. McInerney, district foreman storage, pipe line and sales division; R. B. Walters, safety engineer. B. H. Johnston, district office manager, Oklahoma City district; C. M. Weakley, superintendent of cable tools, drilling department; B. S. Riffe, superintendent rotary tools, drilling department; A. R. Daugherty, welfare and compensation claims department Oklahoma City district; W. W. Clawson, district geologist, Oklahoma City district, and K. A. Covell, chief petroleum engineer.

One of the most spectacular incidents in the Oklahoma City field, pictures of which have been distributed all over the world, was the fire of the Sinclair Oil & Gas Company's Stamper No. 3 which was burning October 10, 1929, when this view was taken. A story of its quenching will be found on another page. Note the melted derrick. Immediately below is a close-up of one of the gigantic motors frequently used in lieu of engines in rotary drilling. It is a General Electric, 200 horsepower. Almost every kind of new equipment found an experiment station in this field. The two boilers are water tubed, a product of Rose Brothers.

The Taming of "Wild Mary"

MANNA no longer falls from the skies, and it has been rather definitely established that money does not grow on trees yet the story of "Wild Mary Sudik" is a true tale of a period when for eleven days and nights substantial golden wealth actually did rain, uncontrolled, upon a substantial area of countryside.

The story of the taming of "Wild Mary" is an oil field epic issuing from the train of scientific oil field development which has written new and unprecedented chapters in oil development history.

Blowing in on the morning of March 26, 1930, with a force that carried twenty joints of heavy drill pipe high into the air and seriously damaged the derrick with which it was drilled, this well for eleven days defied all efforts at control and, during that period, tossed prodigally at the wide world a golden stream valued at approximately $75,-000 for each day of the unhampered flow.

"Wild Mary's" official designation is Mary Sudik No. 1, drilled by Indian Territory Illuminating Oil Company. Springing into being with an unexpected rumble and an unladylike roar, the well caught operators and drilling crew unprepared to cope with the intensity of her emotions. She resisted all preliminary efforts at conciliation or control and, like a spoiled and temperamental queen, ran things practically to suit her whims for ten days, forcing a shutdown of field operations which was virtually general. It was not until caveman tactics were resorted to, on the eleventh day, that her tantrum was subdued and her wasteful extravagance curbed.

This was accomplished by means of special equipment designed and manufactured after all existing curbs had failed. More than 100 workers, garbed in slickers which only partially protected them from the shower of oil, participated in the task made exceedingly hazardous by the ever-present fire menace. One small spark at any time during the period of uncurbed flow would have extended a lake of fire over several square miles of ground. creating an

(Continued on page 38)

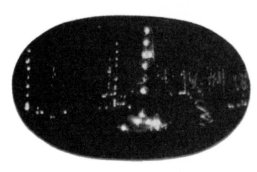

Two years ago Avenue G in Oklahoma City was just another street in Capitol Hill. Now it is a city in itself—one that oil built—with its principal business houses representing equipment firms from all over the world. The top picture is an airplane view. The second scene is another interesting example of the freezing effect of escaping high gas pressure. The pipe, or "blow off" vent, is necessary in this field to relieve the huge pressure. The visitor to Oklahoma City possibly is most impressed with the view of the gigantic field at night, with its millions of electric lights glittering in a miles-long lane of brilliance. Below is a highly improved portable welding outfit for pipe line construction used by the Empire Company.

The Wild Mary Sudik

Lined, not with silver, but rather, with gold are the clouds of crude oil spray with which "Wild Mary Sudik" in petroleate majesty is showering the country roundabout in the panorama, upper left. For eleven days the surrounding derricks in the picture stood idle while operators of the Sudik lease wrestled with this Frankinstein monster of their own creation. The view is taken looking almost directly west. Off to the north, as far as eye can see, stalk columns of steel monsters which might well have illustrated a scene in H. G. Wells' "War of the Worlds." However, unlike the derrick-like fighting machines with which Wells permitted his Martian hordes to invade and lay waste the planet Earth, this army brings Earth-denizens upon whom it casts its shadow prosperity and happiness rather than death and devastation. At the time this picture was taken, the Mary Sudik well marked the extreme southern extremity of the field. The line of derricks headed toward the north extends for seven miles. Since the picture was taken, a similar line of derricks has been extended a considerable distance to the south. Both the upper and lower panoramas afford clear views of the largest and most expensive rotary-drilled oil field in the

world. Much of the equipment now in daily use in this field had never been designed nor manufactured prior to development of this pool. Necessity, created by new and hitherto unexplored drilling conditions, mothered numerous inventions which now are a part of regular stock in drilling supply warehouses that serve the field.

Many equipment firms, scarcely known before, have built business and reputations of national scope by virtue of their connection with activities of this field. Centered, in the lower view is an interesting close-up of a derrick under construction. Close observation reveals two derrick workers perched on the cat-walk which surrounds the crownblock of this derrick. This is a comparatively new phase of steelwork-ing no whit less hazardous than the tasks of those who tread the eye-beams of the steel skeletons that form the framework for modern skyscrapers. Sometimes these workers make a misstep, and when they do it becomes incumbent upon some of their fellows to notify friends and relatives. Interesting among the items

scattered about at the derrick base are the four large boilers "stacked" at the right of the structure. 'Ere long these will be kept hot twenty-four hours a day, seven days a week, supplying steam which sends the long rotary stem on its quest of exploration to the lower strata of the earth's crust.

A splendid view of Oklahoma City's skyline, which also gives an idea of the proximity of the Oklahoma City Oil Field to the business section is shown in the above panorama. At extreme left of picture is the Oklahoma Gas and Electric Company building. In foreground, just left of Baker, Hanna and Blake building is the Cotton Exchange building. Just beyond, where reversed view of pyramid electric sign may be seen, is the Braniff building, back of which looms the Southwestern Bell Telephone tower. Extremely white structure, next to Braniff building is Oklahoma Savings building, next to which is shown a clear view of the Petroleum building, topped by electric sign showing an oil derrick. Just back of this may be seen the Franklin building, owned by Wirt Franklin Petroleum Corporation. Large structure, just back

of Alexander Drug building is the Perrine building, topped by electric sign. Next is the W. T. Hales building. The Colcord, Huckins and Kingkade structure may be identified by designating signs. New Midwest Theater building is seen just to right of Colcord building in the picture. Large building cornering in extreme right is the Kerr Dry Goods building. Close study of the horizon will reveal the steady encroachment of derricks into the valuable real estate areas of the city. Below is a good panorama of the field itself. An interesting comparison may be drawn from some of the small water-well derricks, which although of good size themselves, appear as toys against the towering oil rigs in the background. The square "lakes" seen in the picture are "slush pits" which supply the rotary mud which is continually circulated into the hole as the rotary bits grind their way into the ground. At the right is seen a battery of small tanks which serve as temporary storage. Temporary storage of this nature is erected on each lease to handle the oil produced until it can be turned into the pipeline. The many lease houses which dot the landscape throughout the scene offer an idea of the number of workers employed in this extensive indus-

try. Thousands of workers live at the direct scene of their activities, while thousands of others are quartered in Capitol Hill and in Oklahoma City residence areas north of the river.

Probably no industry in the world takes better care of its workers than the oil industry. A row of neat lease houses in which workers reside may be seen in the foreground of the above panorama. These houses are built by the operating companies and are supplied rent-free to their employees. Electricity, gas and running water all are provided free of cost. The white structure centering on the left hand page, above, is a gasoline, plant of the Wirt Franklin Petroleum Corporation where millions of cubic feet of gas daily are converted into a highly volatile motor fuel—natural gasoline. Millions of gallons of valuable fuel once lost into the air now are reclaimed for commercial use by operation of such plants. The black structures near the plant, resembling tiers of inverted giant cowbells are cooling towers used in process of condensing gas into gasoline. In the left side of the view, at the crossroads, may be seen two field warehouses with racks of drill

pipe resembling stacks of cordwood. To the right may be seen storage tanks, while in the foreground is a field office of Wirt Franklin Petroleum Corporation and Southern Drilling Company.

In the lower view, the giant derricks, "row on row" may be seen stretching away into the distance, while the setting of an oil field in action is rendered complete by the No. 1 Sigmon gusher as it sprays the surrounding countryside with a flood of valuable fluid. A scene which might be likened to Flanders Field where "poppies blow between the crosses, row on row," but a far happier scene, a scene of industry and life rather than of disaster and death. The engines of enterprise rather than engines of destruction are responsible for the shell-torn appearance of the fields. Huge trucks and trailers, carrying tons of drilling equipment, thread their way day and night through mud, oily ooze or hub-deep dust to keep operations in the field supplied with the materials necessary to maintain activity at full blast twenty-four hours a day.

H. V. FOSTER

H. V. Foster, president of the Indian Territory Illuminating Oil Company, entered the oil business when he was twenty-one years old. His first contact came in the handling of a lease on the entire Osage Nation. He has been active in oil development organization and financing throughout his entire business life. Under his leadership, this company, discoverer of the Oklahoma City Oil Field, has attained international prominence. Mr. Foster is a national figure in oil development and financing. His home is in Bartlesville.

A. V. HOENIG

A. V. Hoenig, vice-president in charge of production for the Indian Territory Illuminating Oil Company, hails from the site of the world's first oil well, Titusville, Pennsylvania. Mr. Hoenig has spent thirty-four of his fifty-three years in the oil business and has been associated with a number of prominent companies here and in foreign countries. He came to the I. T. I. O. in 1927. He has had a particularly active part in the development of the field.

(Continued from page 28)

inferno in which even Dante might have known new terrors.

Roar of the escaping gas and oil was plainly audible for several miles, while particles of oil sprayed buildings in Norman, eleven miles to the south and at Nicoma Park, twelve miles east. The spouting plume was visible from office buildings in the capital city, seven miles away.

When preliminary efforts at control proved fruitless, dikes were hastily constructed in an effort to trap as much of the valuable fluid as possible, while new methods were tried.

On the night of March 30, partial control had been obtained by means of a master gate. During that night the well was practically under control, but, early the following morning, sand blast and gas pressure proved too strong for the gate and the petroleum Vesuvius again burst forth, with a flood estimated at 2,000 barrels of oil an hour and 200,000,000 cubic feet of gas a day.

After all other known methods of control had failed, the well was finally capped and oil directed into the tanks on April 6 by means of a 3,000 pound die nipple constructed by the American Iron and Machine Company and designed by Pat Sutton and Clyde Deverse of the I. T. I. O. and H. M. Myracle, Superintendent of the machine works.

Snuffing Colossus' Candle

THE moth attacks the candle's flame and is destroyed. But this is a story of a human moth who attacks the candle of Colossus, extinguishes the flame, emerges with wings only slightly singed, and collects his reward at the box office.

The moth in this case is M. M. Kinley of the Kinley Torpedo Company, who, with his brother, F. T. Kinley, has quenched many an oil field fire throughout the oil producing sections of the United States.

One may question Kinley's judgment and some of the more timorous spectators might question his sanity as he steps

Representative of the group of some 25,000 workers whose industry has contributed to the development of the Oklahoma City field are the four men shown in the above panel. At the top is A. P. Anderson, of the firm of Anderson and Hughes. Cecil Tillman is next, a partner of the drilling firm of Patrick and Tillman. "Eddie" Brauer, one of the four partners that form the Brauer Machine and Supply Company, handlers of oil field equipment, is pictured next. Last is shown W. C. Morgan, once a "canal wrench" engineer, later a tool-dresser and driller and now district manager for the Hughes Tool Company.

into the center of the column of flame, carrying in his arms a charge of nitroglycerine sufficient to destroy a sizeable Oklahoma City building. But none can question his courage nor fail to appreciate his achievement.

Fire is an ever-present hazard in a great oil field. To those familiar with its seriousness it is astounding that so few oil or gas wells escape ignition. However, once ignited, a well becomes a more than ordinarily serious problem. Terrific heat generated by a blazing well forces shutting down of operations all about it, endangers property for hundreds of yards around and sometimes proves extremely costly to owners of the well.

To date, only one such serious fire has occurred in the Oklahoma City pool. On October 8, 1929, the Kinleys were called upon to quench the Sinclair Oil and Gas Company's blazing No. 3 Stamper, a 100,000,000 cubic foot gas well.

For two days and nights the mighty columns of flame lighted up Oklahoma City and the surrounding country for several miles. So bright was the blaze that residents in the north end of the city declare that they were able to sit on front porches and read a newspaper at midnight. The steel derrick withered like a leaf under a blow torch. Clad in asbestos suits, with streams of cold water playing directly upon them as they advanced, the while steam lines played upon the blaze itself, the Kinleys stepped into the flames and cut away, piece by piece, the debris that had been the derrick and drilling rig. To each of these, they attached cables while tractors dragged the crumpled metal away.

With the area cleared of all super-heated metal pieces, they re-entered the blaze and deposited a heavy charge of nitroglycerine at the very heart of the inferno. With all preliminaries completed, the thirty-one quart nitroglycerine cartridge was detonated electrically. The vacuum created at the well-mouth by the concussion snuffed the gigantic torch as one might pinch out a candle between finger and thumb.

The first contractor in this group is H. D. "Cotton" Klintworth, proprietor of the Exchange Drilling Company. Below is Carl Wimberly, field engineer for the Lucey Products Company. Master of his trade and an expert in the myriad complications of deep well drilling is Ed Gladieux, the third individual pictured. Gladieux is proprietor of the company bearing his name. The Rose Drilling Company, another well known unit in the Oklahoma City Field, is captained by Walter W. Rose, owner and manager, whose photograph appears last of the four.

Oil Field Big Electric Current User

MANY motors, lights and other things create a big need for electricity in an oil field. Recognizing this need and ever alert to meet an industrial demand, the Oklahoma Gas and Electric Company, owners of the electric utility franchise in Oklahoma City, installed in March, 1929, a 2,500 Kva. sub-station and two miles of 4 Kv. secondary lines to serve the city field. The gradual growth of the Oklahoma City field has brought it to where it now covers an area of proven territory of approximately forty square miles and the O. G. & E. followed the trend of the productivity until it now has eight substations of 11,500 Kva. capacity and approximately eighteen miles of Kv. secondary lines installed.

The "Grass Roots" Test

FATE plays queer tricks at times.

It was a really unusual one that it played upon L. E. Trout, Oklahoma City chief geologist for the C. C. Julian Oil and Royalty Company, on August 19, 1930, when the Sinclair Oil and Gas Company's No. 5 School Land well blew in for approximately 40,000 barrels of oil a day.

This well is located in NW NW SE 36-11N-3W, at the southern extremity of the field, nearly to the Cleveland County line.

About ten years ago Trout decided he would be a "Wildcatter." He worked his own geology, the initial labor in that part of the county, and got together a block of leases. Financing was extremely difficult at that time, for scarcely anyone believed there really was oil to be had in Oklahoma County. But Trout stayed with it until he got together enough money to drill about 3,500 feet. Nothing happened.

Then the money was gone. So Trout sold an interest to W. B. Green, now dead, so as to continue the test. Green took over the well and drilled a bit further, and then called on W. R. Ramsey, prominent oil man of the capital city, who with his brother, W. E. Ramsey, owns the Ramsey Petroleum Company. Ramsey then took over the operations and drilled further down. But at a total depth of approximately 4,500 feet the hole was abandoned.

Immediately following the discovery of oil in the Oklahoma City field, the Oklahoma Gas and Electric Company constructed lines to the field and erected substations to supply the necessary current. The large Harrah generating plant of the O. G. and E. is shown above, with the newly-completed Belle Isle plant just below. These two plants are of the latest type and are more than adequate to supply Oklahoma City with its approximate population of 200,-000 persons, the adjacent oil fields and numerous other cities in the state. The lower picture displays the new Doheny Stone "Hydril," a hydraulically controlled drilling unit recently introduced into the field.

That was a deep hole for that day and time. In fact tools had not yet been manufactured capable of going much deeper.

When the Sinclair Company began operations on its lease, for which it had paid $77 an acre, believed at the time to be an exorbitant figure, one of the workmen familiar with the history of the early venture remarked, "Those birds must have been crazy to have quit drilling just at the grass roots."

For the "dry hole" which Trout and his associates sunk to the "great" depth of 4,500 feet was less than 100 feet from where the Sinclair No. 1 School Land came in recently as a huge gusher. They failed by 2,000 feet to go deep enough.

Trout now is willing to admit the workman's charge. "I might just as well have been a millionaire as worth what I am today," he says, ruefully.

Bread that Became Cake

BECAUSE Bob Cook and Dot Oatman, vaudeville stars, who in reality are Mr. and Mrs. Bob Cook, had big hearts, as is often true of folk in the theatrical profession, they are wealthy today.

Cook's sister had married a railroad man in Oklahoma City. They had several children. It became necessary for the husband to make a change, he had been transferred to Denison, Texas. Their little home was on a ten-acre tract east of Capitol Hill. They tried to sell it, but real estate dealers and buyers were not interested in Capitol Hill property—at that time. The family, in humble circumstances, stood to lose all they had put into the little home.

Bob came to the rescue. He had some money saved for a rainy day and decided to use it to purchase his sister's place. Bread cast upon the waters.

But in the early summer of 1930 the "bread" came drifting in, all iced up and looking like a gorgeous birthday cake. Heenan and Coe, independent operators, brought in two producers in rapid succession on the Cook place, one for 13,023 barrels and the other for 15,000 barrels initial production daily.

The old days of the "canal wrench" gangs are about numbered since engines of progress such as the one in the top picture dig trenches almost as fast as a man can walk. In case you are wondering, a "canal wrench" is the veteran pipe liner's definition of a shovel. The picture is by courtesy of the Barber Green Ditcher Company and the Southern Construction Company. Next below is a close up of natural gasoline traps on National separators on the Sinclair Oil and Gas Company's Kinter No. 1. Daybreak in the oil field would intrigue any artist. Below is an example of how oil is piped from outlying wells to a central tank assembly.

TOM B. SLICK

Tom B. Slick

"King of Wildcatters"

A MONG the most colorful figures in the history of oil was the late Tom B. Slick, independent operator, who amassed a fortune totalling millions of dollars by taking chances more timorous spirits nervously spurned. Aptly termed by men of oil as "King of Wildcatters" Slick opened more new pools in the Mid-Continent area than probably any other individual operator. Declining the advantages and ease that his vast wealth offered he continued to find an outlet for his dynamic energies in the rigors of the oil fields. He died in August, 1930 at the age of 47 years, leaving behind a fortune variously estimated at from seventy-five to one hundred million dollars as a monument to his courage, his acumen and his energy.

Tom Slick's life story brightens the pages of petroleum history. Born in the shadow of derricks in Clarion, Pennsylvania, he lived his life practically within the oil business. When still in his teens he went to Illinois where he worked as a tool dresser. Thence to Kansas, where he worked for a time in an oil well supply house.

In 1907, he came to Oklahoma where he took a position at $150 a month, buying leases for a large company. Eventually accumulating enough funds to indulge his desire to become an operator in his own right, Slick put down his first wildcat well in what later was to become the great Cushing field. It was a dry hole. Undaunted, he sought additional funds, secured them, drilled again, this time with success. Immediately he leased all available lands in that section. Later he sold his holdings for $2,500,000.

His next move was to drill the discovery well in the field which bears his name, the Slick pool situated near the

The ear splitting din of compressor exhausts from a battery such as shown above can only be ascertained by hearing. These machines "crack" the crude petroleum, liberating the gasoline content. The scene is in an Indian Territory \Illuminating Oil Company plant. The center picture shows a sand trap. One of the worst sources of trouble in the Oklahoma City field is the sand which cuts out massive valves and connections like soft wax. This assembly serves to collect the sand before the oil passes to the separators. Below is the largest rotary drilling motor in the field. It is an Allis-Chalmers and was used by the Hall & Briscoe Company. It develops 300 H. P.

town of Slick, Creek County. Later, he was credited with playing a large part in the development of the Tonkawa field, and with the discovery of the Crosscut Texas, St. Louis Wilcox and Tonkawa deep sands.

"When there's a new field opened up, Tom Slick will be in there," became a watchword with the operators of the oil game. It was like a poker game to Slick. He played, not for the joy of winning, but for the joy of playing.

His major deal came on March 1, 1929, when he sold one-half interest in his holdings to the Prairie Oil & Gas Company, for a reputed sum of $40,000,000, one of the largest deals ever consummated in the oil industry. And withal, when his will was recently probated, the remainder of his holdings were estimated at ranging from $75,000,000 to $100,000,000.

One of the most interesting chapters in Tom B. Slick's life was the fight that he made in defense of the independent oil operators, especially the little fellow, in the Seminole area. The initial pro-ration program was under discussion. Some companies apparently were attempting to bring about a disadvantage for the little fellows, but Slick appeared before the Oklahoma Corporation Commission and forcefully advanced his views.

"You want me to pinch down my wells until you can get a chance to get your's dug so that you can take some of my oil," he told them. "Well, you can't do it! If any pinching down is going to be done, all the wells in Oklahoma will be pinched down for twenty-four hours, say, on Sunday so the field men can have a rest."

He maintained that no court, no law can prevent a man from taking oil out of the ground he owns or leases, and he finally forced the larger companies to concede his point. The equal proration schedule now in force in Oklahoma was the result.

Despite the fact that Slick sold one-half of his holdings in 1929 to the Prairie, at the time of his untimely death

Oil field parlance terms the top picture a "Christmas Tree," due to the many branch outlets provided for the flow of thousands of barrels of oil under excessive gas pressure. When boilers are to be moved, they move 'em in bunches as is graphically portrayed in the second scene shown by courtesy of the manufacturers of Martin eight wheel wagons. "Pick-a-back" shops are virtually necessary. The next to last scene is on a Wirt Franklin lease effecting an emergency fitting. If the sometimes 250,000,000 cubic feet gas pressure was released direct to your stove it might go through some peculiar contortions. To reduce pressure, the Pioneer Gas Company has built the complicated affair below.

he perhaps was the second largest operator in the Oklahoma City field. As of August 27th, 1930, the Tom B. Slick estate had forty-five producing wells in the South Oklahoma City field in which a majority of the interest was owned, entirely exclusive of these shared equally with the Prairie. Also, thirty-three wells were drilling on that date.

The first big producer that the Slick estate brought in here was the No. 1 Glidden, spudded in on July 4, 1929, and coming in on October 3, 1929, for an initial production of approximately 15,000 barrels.

The largest well the Slick estate has brought in was the No. 1 Campbell, which came in after Slick's death for approximately 40,000 barrels daily. Potential daily production of the Slick wells in the Oklahoma City area was estimated at 350,000 barrels, predicted upon the initial production of each well.

The Slick estate at this time owns thousands of acres of leases in Oklahoma County, and many, many thousands of acres in practically all other parts of the state, not to mention its out-of-state operations. Approximately 5,000 acres west of Edmond are under lease at this time.

Officials of the Slick Company include Charles F. Urschel, who is the ranking head of the firm, carrying the title of general manager, a resident of Oklahoma City and a brother-in-law of Mr. Slick; E. E. Kirkpatrick, in charge of the Tulsa office; C. W. Baker, general superintendent; W. N. Stokes, general counsel; H. S. Thomas, chief geologist; J. H. Grand, head of the legal department; C. M. Howell, office manager and head of the accounting division. E. I. Irwin, head of the land department; B. N. Wright, head of the purchasing department, and Guy Hannum, lease buyer.

It was announced recently that Mrs. Tom B. Slick, Mr. Urschel and Mr. Kirkpatrick will continue the operations of the late "King of Wildcatters' " holdings.

An idea of the number of lengths of drill stem needed to drill a deep hole in the Oklahoma City Field is gained from the above picture. In the foreground is the rotary table and well hole. The second view is the Oklahoma City plant of the Spengler Tool Company, manufacturers of general oil field equipment. The monster chain in the third picture is the driving force for the rotary tables, also manufactured by Spengler. Below is a shop scene with a pile of cone forgings in the foreground from which the saw-toothed drilling cones are cut. This also is a view of the local Spengler plant.

Two veterans in oil prospecting in the Oklahoma City area are Lev. H. Prichard, president of the Anderson Prichard Oil Corporation, and J. Steve Anderson, vice-president. Originally owners of several thousand acres in what is now the Oklahoma City oil field, this organization still owned considerable acreage when discovery well of the I. T. I. O. Company spudded in. As the test well progressed, they added to these holdings and they now own extensive interests in many valuable producing properties in the field.

J. STEVE ANDERSON

LEV. H. PRICHARD

Anderson-Prichard Oil Corporation

VETERANS in the Oklahoma City oil field and in the oil business in Oklahoma, generally, are J. Steve Anderson and Lev. H. Prichard of the Anderson-Prichard Oil Corporation, with main offices in the Colcord Building, Oklahoma City.

In 1923 and 1924 these men leased up several thousand acres southeast of the city in what now is the South Oklahoma City field.

When the I. T. I. O. began drilling the discovery well of the field, Anderson-Prichard still had a portion of the leases they had secured some four or five years previously. And, they set out to get more. Their knowledge of the situation in the district, obtained when they previously had bought up leases, enabled them quickly to secure new leases of a desirable nature.

Of the first batch of leases secured an eighty-acre lease known as the Hoopes lease was one that Anderson-Prichard retained. In 1929 they entered into a contract with Tom B. Slick to develop the Hoopes lease for a one-half interest. This lease now has eight producing wells upon it. Anderson-Prichard took leases in the north end of the south field around the pest house, getting approximately a quarter section, including the eleven acre pest house lease. The No. 1 Pest House was the first well that the company brought in on this group of leases, this well coming in on August 25, 1930, for approximately 12,000 barrels daily.

On November 1, the company had eighteen completed wells with a potential daily production of 172,000 barrels and had eight wells drilling.

Hinderliter Tool Company has had an important part in development of new tools and equipment demanded in this phenomenal field. Top picture is a factory scene showing thousands of drill bits and other equipment being rushed to completion for use in the Oklahoma City field. Second picture shows a new method of reaming drill hole to keep it straight. Third is a view of the famous "mud-hog." This one is made by Wilson-Snyder. Last scene is a valve and outlet set-up to control a monster well. This is shown by courtesy of Kero-Test Company.

A story of dogged persistence in the face of repeated disappointments and civic ambition that equalled the desire for financial gain that prompts oil exploration and development is woven into the history of prospecting for oil in Oklahoma County. For years, W. R. Ramsey and W. E. Ramsey, brothers, who operate as the Ramsey Petroleum Corporation, have delved into the corners and depths of the county, seeking to discover an oil pool. In this, time and their own actions have

W. R. RAMSEY

repeatedly proven that pride of civic achievement in the opening of such a pool would have equalled and probably overshadowed the satisfaction gained from a successful financial venture. Their faith in the potentialities of this area was rewarded in material form when opening of the Oklahoma City Field found them in possession of valuable acreage in the producing area.

W. E. RAMSEY

Ramsey Petroleum Corporation

THE name of the Ramsey Petroleum Corporation is well known in the oil fraternity. To W. R. and W. E. Ramsey, long residents of Oklahoma City, has gone much credit for early attempts to discover oil in Oklahoma County. And these two brothers have bought up much acreage in the county at various times. When the big oil boom started here late in 1928, with the discovery well, it had not caught the Ramseys napping.

They had considerable acreage and began drilling two wells on their Fortson lease. But before they completed either of these wells the Mid-Kansas Oil & Gas Company, Tulsa, offered the Ramseys $2,000,000 for their holdings in the Oklahoma City field. They accepted, and the Mid-Kansas since has operated the former Ramsey holdings and has added to them. The deal was consummated in February, 1929.

Included were 290 acres of leases and the Nos. 1 and 2 Fortson wells, the former already down to a depth of about 3,500 feet.

That Mid-Kansas made a wise deal was indicated when the No. 2 Fortson came in on June 27, 1929, for a daily production of 6,735 barrels, followed less than a month later by No. 1 Fortson, for 3,165 barrels daily.

Since those two wells came in Mid-Kansas has sunk Nos. 3, 4 and 5 Fortson and Nos. 1 and 2 Browning. Three wells have been completed on the Mollman lease, with another now drilling. And the No. 1 Trosper-Browning, owned jointly by Mid-Kansas and I. T. I. O., is being drilled.

Since the consummation of the deal with the Ramsey brothers, Mid-Kansas has purchased approximately 10,600 acres of leases in the Nicoma Park district, twelve miles east of the city. It has brought in one producer out there, the No. 1 E. B. Trosper, which came in for 215 barrels daily, on December 12, 1929. Two dry holes have been hit in that section, but Mid-Kansas is giving the district

One of the prominent drilling companies in the field is represented by Tom Phillips, the first above, a partner in the combination of Mead and Phillips. A perfect soldier of fortune type is "Bunk" Henderson, a toolpusher for the Capitol Drilling Company. His fanciful tales are accepted with whatever degree of veracity the hearer is pleased to grant, but, withal they are interesting, and "Bunk" is a welcome visitor wherever he goes. The "Four Horsemen" in the third picture braved inclemency and muddy going last winter, choosing horses in lieu of the difficulties encountered by a car in the last view. The chauffeur is scanning the sea of mud for possible rescue.

W. G. SKELLY

One of the most interesting as well as one of the most active independent operators in the Mid-Continent Oil area is W. G. Skelly, founder and head of the
Skelly Oil Company of Tulsa. Strenuous nature of his activities as president
of the vast producing, refining and marketing organization which bears his name
has not prevented Mr. Skelly from indulging an active interest in politics and he
at present is republican national committeeman from Oklahoma. While a War-
wick in politics, Mr. Skelly never has sought office for himself although
he has been importuned on many occasions to seek national political honors.

a thorough test and has recently started the No. 1 V. R. Ball on a new location. Also, this company has purchased about 4,500 acres of leases in the territory west of Edmond, in the north end of the county, where it is drilling the No. 1 Agnes Messer, which recently came in for production just below 6,700 feet in the Wilcox sand, opening an entirely new pool in Oklahoma county.

Mid-Kansas is a subsidiary of the Ohio Oil Company, which just recently took over the Transcontinental, which operates a number of filling stations in Oklahoma City and elsewhere. The company operates three refineries, one at Fort Worth, Texas, and at Bristow and Boynton, Oklahoma.

J. J. Frommer is superintendent of production in the Oklahoma City district, and Alex Stepanoff is the chief geologist for the district.

Skelly Oil Company

AMONG the large independents operating in the Oklahoma City Field is the Skelly Oil Company of Tulsa, which although it entered the field later than a number of others now has extensive and valuable holdings. With operations on nine leases, the company has sixteen producing wells with five more drilling. Most productive of these operations is the Mary E. Hoopes tract of eighty acres on which 8 producing wells are situated.

Skelly Oil Company was founded in Tulsa by W. G. Skelly on October 10, 1919. Mr. Skelly, who was a drilling contractor before he became a large oil producer and refiner had been active in the fields of Pennsylvania; Ohio; Indiana; Illinois; Wichita Falls, Texas; Healdton; Oklahoma; and Eldorado, Kansas, before establishing his present organization at Tulsa.

Operations of Skelly Oil Company today extend throughout the entire Mid-Continent area, including nearly all major pools of Oklahoma, Kansas and Texas. Production of "natural" or "casinghead" gasoline from natural gas has been developed to a high degree by this company and its natural gasoline plants are found in many fields—old and new. Another important development has been that of "Skelgas" a compressed natural gas in metal cartridges for use in areas where piped natural gas is not available.

"Dog House" Rowland, the first above, is connected with the Star Manufacturing Company of Oklahoma City. Not many know his first name. He supplies derrick foundations, and the small iron tool houses necessary to every rig. These are known as "dog houses." The next below is W. M. Payne, head of the Payne Drilling Company which has drilled several wells in the field. The third overcoated figure is Jack C. Shaffer, also owner of several rigs in the field and himself a producer. Harry C. Disler, superintendent of the Carter Oil Company, is the last face in the panel.

Much has been written about that fraternity of men who work in steel. There is another fraternity, its stipulations and certificates of membership just as stringent—men in oil. Although they technically are in the same category as men in steel, there is a certain camaraderie about men in oil which places them in a well defined class, with their own nicknames, jargon, and friendships held true and fast from Russian steppes to South American Tropics. At the top, left to right, is one group bossed by V. Goad, driller, on location at the I. T. I. O. Eacock No. 2, for the Fesemyer Drilling Company. Next is a "tour" of the Mabee and Blackstock Drilling Company with J. S. Yarbrough as head man, standing next to the drill stem on the left. H. C. Floyd is the chief driller for the Exchange Drilling Company, standing on the left, with his hat removed, Charles Walton, second from the left, is the "boss" of this crew on the Anderson and Kerr Company's Viewpoint No. 2, location. The right center scene is an Olsen Drilling Company crew, on rig No. 16, on an Anderson-Prichard location. Albert Ashbrener is the head driller on the left. On the lower row, left to right, A. Monroe, second from the left, is head driller for Schoenfeld and Hunter, contractors. A. Manahan crew is represented by W. E. Bufkin as boss driller on the left. In the last picture L. C. (Red) Morter, partner in the Morter Drilling Company, is standing on the extreme left next to his boss driller, W. G. Walkup, on an I. T. I. O. location. All tools in these pictures are developments of the Hughes Tool Company.

A Stiff Pro-ration Schedule

IT HAS been said elsewhere in this volume that the Oklahoma City oil field has set whatever records of production it has been able to make in the face of the most stringent pro-ration schedule the oil world yet has seen.

In September, 1929, the operators got together to discuss this move. Wirt Franklin, of the Wirt Franklin Petroleum Corporation, was a moving factor in this schedule. The Indian Territory Illuminating Oil Company, discoverers of the south city field, were also actively engaged in the move and in giving 100 percent co-operation throughout. Many other companies have given splendid co-operation, and through this move, the Oklahoma City field has borne more than its share of the brunt of keeping the market from becoming even more glutted than it now is.

On September 12, 1929, as result of these conservation conferences, the Oklahoma City field went under a complete shutdown schedule for a month, or until October 12. Then all producing wells were allowed to run full time until October 27. They then were shut down for one day between October 27 and November 1. From November 1 to December 1 they operated on a basis of 60 percent production. From December 1 to January 1, 1930, a 50 percent basis also was maintained.

From January 1 to January 21, 1930, a 50 percent basis also was maintained. Then until February 26 the wells were allowed to produce only 25 percent. From February 26 to April 15 the reduction was down to $12\frac{1}{2}$ percent, and from April 15 to June 26 a $16\frac{2}{3}$ percent production was permitted. From June 26 to July 8 only $8\frac{1}{3}$ percent production was allowed.

The period from July 8 to July 24 saw a complete shutdown, and then on the latter date a resumption of the $8\frac{1}{3}$ percent basis was seen. A three-day shutdown was had on August 9, 10, and 11, when again the $8\frac{1}{3}$ percent basis was continued.

Otto Bradford, formerly a resident of Ardmore and an oil man with much experience behind him, was selected as umpire of the field to see that the proration schedule was carried out.

Ira G. Watkins is big, therefore his nickname is "Big Boy." He is the owner and operator of several drilling rigs under the banner of the Watkins Drilling Company. Next below is E. Trippe, tool pusher for the Manhattan Drilling Company. On the left in the third is Guy Danielson, representative for the Brauer Company, who in his rounds of the field, is never without his camera. Mr. Danielson has taken hundreds of pictures of oil fields and oil field characters all over the United States and Mexico. The pictures on the preceding five pages were taken by him. On his right is J. J. Frommer, superintendent of the Mid-Kansas Oil and Gas Company. Below is Harris, German police dog, brought here by a driller returning from the Rumanian field.

Coline Oil Company

LATE in 1926 the Coline Oil Company acquired a block of leases in the South Oklahoma City field. It spudded in its first well on December 28, 1928, and brought it in as a producer on June 27, 1929. Since then it has drilled thirty-five other wells, 33 of which also are producing at this time. These producing wells have a daily potential production of approximately 100,000 barrels of high grade oil. Coline has altogether 520 acres of leases in the Oklahoma City field. It has storage capacity in the field totaling 285,000 barrels.

Its main offices are in Oklahoma City, in the Tradesmen Bank Building, H. L. Briggs is vice-president and general manager, and P. E. Williams is general superintendent in charge of production. E. A. Paschal, who is mentioned elsewhere in connection with the early efforts of tracing the geology of the field, is chief geologist.

Shell Petroleum Corporation

SHELL PETROLEUM CORPORATION is a company in the Shell Union, which is the operating company in the United States of the Royal Dutch Shell Company of Holland.

This firm was one of the first to buy leases in the Oklahoma City field, purchasing its first group on December 3, 1926. Its first well in the field came in on September 11, 1929. This was the Petty No. 1, in NW NE 30-11N-2W. Since that time Shell has brought in six additional wells on the Petty lease, and one on the Edgemier lease, making a total of eight producers this firm has in the South Oklahoma City field.

Shell also has approximately 20,000 acres of land under lease in Oklahoma County. It runs its oil through its own pipe lines, operating under the subsidiary of the Shell Union. A 25,000,000 cubic feet daily capacity gasoline plant is operated on the Petty lease.

Officials of the company in the Oklahoma City district are: W. C. Bean, district geologist; C. R. Hargiss, in charge of the district land department; W. M. Gholson, production superintendent for the district, and George Kingelin, district production engineer.

Transportation, obviously, is the motif of these pictures. At the top is shown the modern method in moving a house. Half a hundred horses under the hood of the truck in the next scene replace as many in the flesh in moving one of the largest portable tanks in the field. Cities Service Company, parent company of the Indian Territory Illuminating Oil Company, recently completed a pipe line more than fifty miles long to carry gas from the field. The third scene affords an idea of the magnitude of such a project. Several tons of drill pipe are delivered to a new location on time with the special assembly presented in the lower picture, used by Wagnon Brothers Truck Company.

Prairie Oil and Gas Company

PRAIRIE OIL AND GAS COMPANY did not enter the Oklahoma City field "by right of conquest," so to speak, but instead, bought in after the field was well under development. On March 1, 1929, the Prairie entered here through the consummation of the largest individual deal yet made in the Oklahoma City section. It purchased a one-half interest in the properties of Tom B. Slick, "King of Wildcatters," for what generally was reported at the time as $40,000,000.

This deal involved approximately 8,000 acres of leases in Oklahoma County, and several producing wells.

As of January 1, 1931, the Prairie Oil and Gas Company, in conjunction with Tom B. Slick, now deceased, had a number of producing wells in the field. The potential production of these producers was approximately 50,000 barrels daily.

Main offices of Prairie are at Independence, Kansas, but its Oklahoma City offices are in the Colcord Building. C. W. Chancellor is the district agent here and Sam LeBaron is district superintendent.

Phillips Petroleum Corporation

ANOTHER of the pioneers in the Oklahoma City field, so far as acreage is concerned was the Phillips Petroleum Corporation. This firm acquired its first leases in the vicinity of the south field at about the same time that the I. T. I. O. took its block of leases. However, Phillips first leases were taken in the extreme northern end of Cleveland County, joining the south city field. Later this company acquired other leases in Oklahoma County, and today it has approximately 735 acres under lease in producing territory, and approximately 10,900 acres in other parts of the county.

Although Phillips has not drilled as extensively in this field as some other major operators, it had five oil producers on November 1, 1930, twenty-four wells drilling and owned joint interests in several other operations.

W. F. Smoots is in charge of the land department of the Phillips Petroleum Corp. in the Oklahoma City district.

Gas pressure of two hundred million cubic feet is dangerous. In the lower right hand corner of the first picture above are two long rods attached to valves. These extend several feet from the well and are utilized opening or closing the gas and oil flow. Center picture is a cellar scene. Hughest Tool Company developed fittings seen in this picture. Below is James Barron, who, before his death, was district manager for Henry L. Doherty & Co., and the "Grover Whalen" of the Oklahoma City field. Mr. Barron personally greeted and piloted more than 3,000 guests through the field. Included in this group were business and financial leaders and industrial captains from practically every country in the civilized world.

Among the group of oil luminaries who added to their already established fame and fortune through operations in the Oklahoma City pool is James E. Kessler. Kessler is president of Kessler Petroleum Corporation, Kessler Oil Company and recently paid $1,000,000 for a half interest in the Hall Briscoe organization, taking over the interests of F. C. Hall who retired.

JAMES E. KESSLER

Powell Briscoe, with his former partner, F. C. Hall, long has been active in the Chickasha area. Of approximately 130 wells drilled by Hall and Briscoe, less than one-half dozen were dry. The firm first attracted attention in the Oklahoma City field when its No. 1 Childs well was drilled in, proving up an area that prior to that time had been considered too far west to be productive.

POWELL BRISCOE

One Who Made The Grade

EIGHTEEN years ago James M. Kessler was a soda dispenser in the Veazey Drug store on West Main street. Today he is a self-made millionaire. He was forty years old on August 5, 1930. Another of the romances of the oil game.

Born back in Kentucky in 1890, "Jim" Kessler was one of eleven children, five boys and six girls. Everyone knows what happens financially to a boy reared in a family under such circumstances. It was ultimately a case of "getting out on his own." Kessler did.

The family had moved to Bridgeport, Oklahoma, in 1905 and in 1912 "Jim" came to Oklahoma City. He was just twenty-two years old and had about $5 in his pocket when he reached the city. He went to work at Veazey's as a "soda jerker" and drug clerk. After working there for two years he became a part owner of a drug store at Edmond, in the northern end of the county. He stayed there another two years and then, in 1916, sold out his interest to enter the oil game.

For the next six years he was financial agent for the Noco Petroleum Corporation and the North American Oil Company, with offices in New York City. He left this position to return to Oklahoma, settling at Okmulgee.

His next move was to organize the Kessler Oil Company. This firm operated successfully in Oklahoma, Texas and New Mexico. Six years later he organized the Kessler Petroleum Corporation, which assumed the operation of the Kessler Oil Company properties and other syndicate holdings.

The Kessler companies are given credit for opening the Leck field in Winkler County, Texas, where the discovery well was a 12,000 barrel gusher. The firm still owns the eighty-acre discovery lease, considered the best in that district.

It was on Kessler's fortieth birthday that he purchased the interests of F. C. Hall in the firm of Hall and Briscoe, called the "Damon and Pythias" combination of the Oklahoma City oil field.

The deal was consummated on a basis of a consideration of approximately $1,500,000, part cash, part oil and assumption of obligations. Properties included in the deal consisted of 160 acres of proved and semi-proved leases; forty-

Conception of the massive equipment necessary in the Oklahoma City field is gained from a study of the first of the above pictures, a view of a chain driven sand reel, water cooled, used in bailing, and the second, a double brake calf hoist with heavy cable used in cable tool drilling. The third scene is a new oil bath rotary showing the upper end of the squared kelley which gives purchase to the rotary table in turning the entire string of drill pipe. All pictures are by the courtesy of the International Derrick and Equipment Company whose Oklahoma City warehouse in the field is shown below.

One of those "once in a million" pictures that newspaper photographers dream about is the action view of the No. 1 Vencl well shown upper center. The view was snapped just as the first head of rotary mud, pushed by a gas pressure of millions of cubic feet, welled forth. A few minutes after it was taken, thousands of barrels of oil were gushing from this hole over the surrounding countryside. Upper left shows how workers in the field live while upper right depicts how sandblast in a gusher gnawed away a master valve. In the center two National Tanks are rigged to separate casinghead gasoline, gas and crude oil. Lower left shows a new method of controlling a gusher by shunting the flow through by-pass standpipes. Right view shows a drilling well as it appears at night.

eight acres in SW 25-12N-3W; four producing wells and eight wells drilling at that time. The producers included the No. 1 Childs, Nos. 1 and 2 Lindsey, and the No. 1 Holmes, all completed as big producers. The No. 3 Lindsey was being drilled at the time the deal was closed, as were the No. 1 Mueller and six wells on the Holmes lease. A half interest in drilling tools and equipment valued at $400,000 also was included in the properties passing into Kessler's hands.

Kessler at the same time offered to buy out the holdings of Powell Briscoe, the "Pythias" of the Hall-Briscoe combination, but Briscoe declined to sell. Hall is an older man than either Kessler or Briscoe and plans to retire from active participation in the oil business.

Kessler announced when the deal was consummated there would be no change in the operation of the firm of Hall and Briscoe. The firm's name will not be changed. "Jim" announced he merely would send one of his geologists and one of his engineers to work in the Hall and Briscoe offices in the Commerce Exchange Building. Kessler's offices are in the eighteen-story Petroleum Building, which houses many of the major oil operators in the Oklahoma City field.

That Kessler's confidence in the continuance of the operation of the Hall and Briscoe business is not misplaced would seem to be evidenced by the splendid success that firm has enjoyed. The "Damon and Pythias" combination gained a reputation as "hard and fast traders" in the early days of the Oklahoma City field. Shortly after the discovery well came in they came here from Chickasha, their home, in an airplane and secured the Holmes lease from Mrs. Jeanette Lewis Holmes, sixty acres, and the acre and one-half Childs lease, both considered at the time as "too far west." But it all is in proven territory now. Hall and Briscoe have drilled approximately 130 wells, with less than one-half dozen dry holes to mar their record.

Sinclair Oil and Gas Company

ONE of the larger companies operating in the South Oklahoma City field is the Sinclair Oil and Gas Company. This firm obtained its school land leases in the field early in 1928.

Nerves of steel and agility of monkeys are necessary to the men who clamber over the derrick to handle drill stem shown stacked in picture above. Century Petroleum Company's No. 1 Wyatt gusher is shown blowing oil high over the derrick in second picture. Roy S. Randerson, president of Century Petroleum Company, appears below and lower picture affords a good view of tremendous height of derricks used in the field. This one is 122 feet high.

Rearing its massive tower 32 stories above the street level, the new home of the First National Bank and Trust Company, shown in the architects sketch above, will be the tallest cloud-brusher yet erected in Oklahoma City upon its completion in 1931. Oil has played its part both directly and indirectly in bringing to realization the dream-home long visualized by one of the southwest's largest banking institutions. Expansive development of the Oklahoma City field and subsequent more rapid development of general business in Oklahoma City brought actual construction of this structure considerably ahead of the period for which it had been planned.

As of November 1, 1930, Sinclair had fifty-three producing wells in the Oklahoma City field. In addition, Sinclair had 930 acres of land under lease in productive areas, with about 800 acres leased in outside wildcat areas.

Glen Harroun is district superintendent for Sinclair in the Oklahoma City territory, while John E. VanDall, geologist who worked the structures in Oklahoma County early in the history of the field, is district geologist. Offices are maintained in the Braniff Building.

Many Other Companies In Field

THERE are many other companies operating in the Oklahoma City field that have not as yet been mentioned. In most instances these miscellaneous companies have from one to four locations. They follow:

Acme Gas and Oil Company; Briggs Oil Company; Blackstock and Mabee; British American Oil Company; California Operating Company; Capital City Oil Corporation; Cargill Brothers, Inc.; Century Petroleum Company; Continental Oil Company; Cunard Oil Company; Citizens Oil Company; Deusch and Dietz; Denver Producing and Refining Company; Don Leon Oil Company; Empire Oil and Refining Company. Glidden Oil Company; Gand and Garvin. Government Petroleum Company; J. H. Gwin Drilling Company; Huddleston and McKeehan; L. C. Hivick; Head Petroleum Corporation; Indian State Oil Company; Independent Oil and Gas Company; Ivanhoe Oil and Gas Company. C. C. Julian Oil and Royalty Company; Jones Brothers and Blackwell Oil and Gas Company; Kedberg Oil Company; V. A. Kendy; Liberty Royalties Corporation; John E. Mabee; Minnehoma Oil Company; Morgan Petroleum Company; Oils Incorporated; Oklahoma City Petroleum Corporation; Oil Development Company; Oil State Petroleum Company; Pandem Oil Company; Park Oil and Gas Company; Pace Petroleum Corporation; Plains Petroleum Company; Russell Petroleum Company; Ryan Consolidated Oil Company; Standish-McCluney-Wade; Scott and Company; Spears Drilling Company; C. E. Stout. Jack Shaffer; Traders Oil and Gas Company; George D. Warr; Wrightsmith Oil Company; and H. B. Van Hooser.

A battery of tanks in readiness for an anticipated gusher is shown above. Second picture shows a group of Universal Oil Well Cementing Company trucks especially equipped for pumping cement to the bottom of mile-deep wells. A gasoline plant, floodlighted to facilitate operations, is next shown. This one was equipped by Tulsa Type Boiler and Machinery Company. Steel rotary hose assembly is shown in next view by courtesy of Champion and Barber. Group of bolted storage tanks shown below was provided by Black, Sivalls and Bryson.

Here are nineteen reasons why those identified with the romance of oil continue to be gripped by its peculiar fascination. The matchless thrill that a spouting gusher engenders seems never to lose its edge. The anticipation that immediately precedes the activity of a well that is on the verge of being brought into production, and the realization that comes as the golden flood goes over the top, are sensations that only those who have experienced them can fully appreciate. Back of each of these pictures is a story. The revival of abandoned hopes, the elimination of poverty and pinched circumstances, the reward of patient struggle, are themes woven into many a story behind the scenes.

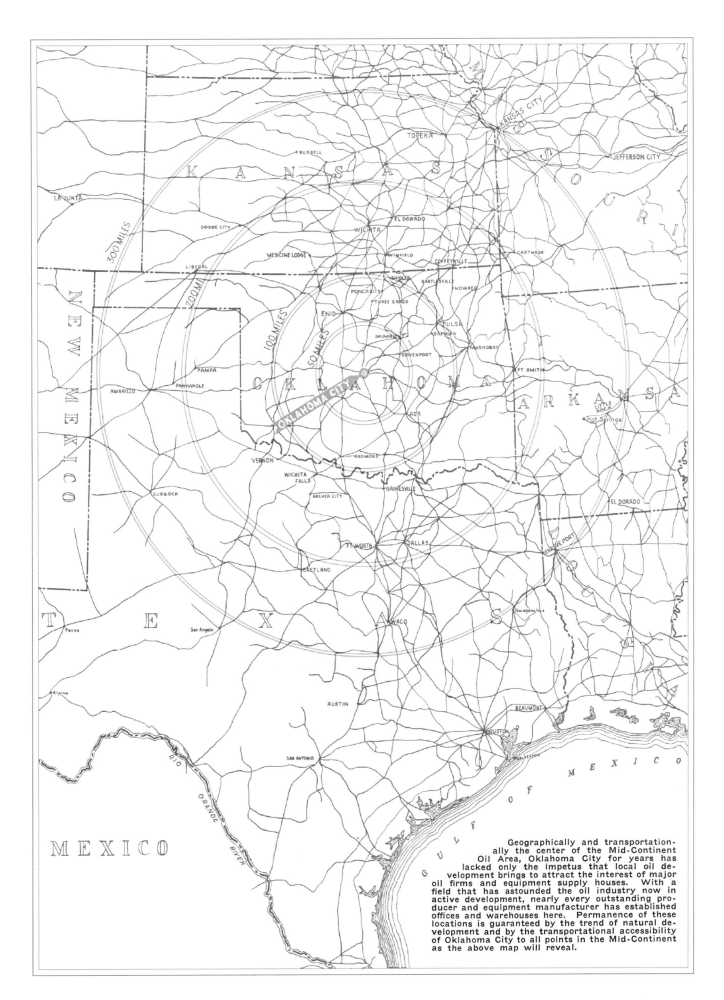

Geographically and transportation-
ally the center of the Mid-Continent
Oil Area, Oklahoma City for years has
lacked only the impetus that local oil development brings to attract the interest of major
oil firms and equipment supply houses. With a
field that has astounded the oil industry now in
active development, nearly every outstanding producer and equipment manufacturer has established
offices and warehouses here. Permanence of these
locations is guaranteed by the trend of natural development and by the transportational accessibility
of Oklahoma City to all points in the Mid-Continent
as the above map will reveal.

Oil and Gas in Oklahoma:
A Legacy of Leadership

In 1934, when this book was originally published, the oil and gas industry in Oklahoma was at a turning point. Behind were the giddy years of seemingly endless gushers and unbridled boomtowns. Ahead were the difficult days of declining prices and deeper fields.

Today, as this book goes to press for a second time through the generosity of Chesapeake Energy Corporation, Oklahoma is still oil and gas country. The difficult times of the 1930s, the 1950s, and the 1980s have come and gone, but left behind have been lessons learned and a legacy that defines the Oklahoma spirit.

What does that legacy mean for Oklahoma?

The most obvious impact of oil and gas on our history is economic. As wildcatters and drillers scrambled over the hills of Oklahoma after 1898, they immediately created jobs and stimulated local economies through the sale of pipe, timber, and tools. Over the long haul, the search for and production of oil and gas attracted workers and investors from other regions of the world and filled the coffers of banks and businesses with the financial capital so desperately needed on the frontier.

As cities and towns grew on this nurturing sustenance of economic stimulation, the men and women who had found the oil and gas invested in the quality of life for those around them. In that first generation were philanthropists such as E.W. Marland, Lloyd Noble, and the Phillips brothers, Frank, L.E., and Waite, who left their mark with the Philbrook Museum, the Woolaroc Museum, and the Frank Phillips Home in Bartlesville.

The next generation of oil and gas community leaders included men such as John Kirkpatrick, whose legacy survives in the Oklahoma City Art Museum, Lyric Theatre, and Omniplex, Dean McGee and Robert S. Kerr, whose commitment to downtown Oklahoma City at a critical time opened doors to projects such as MAPS and the Myriad Gardens.

Today, this legacy of stimulating the economy in the short term and improving the quality of life in the long term still characterizes the oil and gas industry in Oklahoma. The former can be seen in rising state and local revenues, revitalization of downtowns, and record numbers of jobs. The latter comes through the generous contributions and leadership of the current generation of oil and gas pioneers at Chesapeake, Devon, Kerr-McGee, and Conoco-Phillips. Under their watch, the oil and gas industry has found stability as well as vitality, while their actions continue to improve the quality of life every day. That is a legacy of leadership.

— Bob L. Blackburn, Ph.D.